To
Barbara Urbanick
Thanks for helping
my acting back !
Robert B.
Ron Scarberry

Inside of Me

Inside of Me

by
Robert B. Jackson

Illustrated
by
Ronald Scarbough

Published by
Stratford Publishing Company, Inc.
11000 West McNichols, Suite 110
Detroit, Michigan 48221

Printed by Harlo Press, 50 Victor, Detroit, MI 48203

Table of Contents

EACH OTHER

I'd love to have a father,
A sister, or a brother.
All I have is my mother,
But we've got each other.
Mom is wonderful to me.
She is my mother,
My father,
My sister,
And my brother.
We're on welfare, but we care.
We care about our friends,
Our neighbors, and others.
We care about
The way we live each day,
And it won't always be this way.
We're in this world alone,
But we're going to make it
On our own.
Just wait and see,
Someday I'll make Mom proud
Of me.
I only have a mother,
But we've got each other.

QUESTIONS AND ACTIVITIES

1. How many people does it take to be a family?

2. What does the author mean when he says, "She is my father, my sister, and my brother?"

3. What does the author mean when he says, "We're on welfare, but we care?"

4. What does the child want to do for his/her mother?

5. There is a line in the poem that reads, "We're in this world alone." Are they in this world alone? What does the author mean?

6. Do you think the child and his/her mother will "make it"? Why or why not?

7. What is the main idea of the poem?

8. In one sentence, write something you have learned from the poem.

9. Extra, draw an illustration from the poem.

BLACK AND WHITE

Black people don't want
To be black,
And white people don't want
To be white.
Maybe one day
We'll all see the light.
Black people apply
All kinds of ridiculous creams
To their skins.
Hoping it will make them
Lighter, brighter,
Or better yet, whiter.
White people bask foolishly
In the torrid blazing sun
Day after day;
Trying to get a tan
As dark as they can.
There are many things
In this world
That we need to change,
But one of them
Is not our color.
We need to change the way
We treat each other.
When we learn to be kind
And gentle to each other,
The entire world
Will be one color.

QUESTIONS AND ACTIVITIES

1. Have you ever wanted to have lighter or darker skin? If so, why?

2. Why do you suppose some people want a suntan?

3. Can Black people get a suntan?

4. Many people lie in the sun to get a tan. Is this good for their skin?

5. What does the author say we need to change?

6. What do you feel the author means in the last four lines?

7. What is the main idea of the poem?

8. In one sentence, write something you have learned from the poem.

LATINO AND PROUD

I just enrolled in a brand new school.
I'm eager to learn
And ready to obey the rules.
I'm very intelligent and bright
And I want everyone to know,
I'm proud to be a Latino.
I've only been here a few short days,
But I'm working very hard
To learn the new customs and ways.
My English is not so very good.
So, please forgive me, if I'm misunderstood.
All I want is a chance to learn and grow.
I can't speak English well,
But I'm not slow.
Sometimes, I get very confused
And don't understand what to do,
But I realize most students
Only have to speak one language
While I'm trying to speak two.

QUESTIONS AND ACTIVITIES

1. Explain the word Latino.

2. Have you ever been somewhere and people were speaking a language you could not understand? If so, how did you feel?

3. Why do you think some students have trouble learning in school?

4. Have you ever tried to speak a different language? If so, was it easy or difficult to do? Tell us about your experience.

5. Is it an advantage or disadvantage to speak more than one language? Explain your answer.

6. What can you do to help a student who is having difficulty learning because he/she can't speak English well?

7. What is the main idea of the poem?

8. In one sentence, write something you have learned from the poem.

9. Extra, draw an illustration from the poem.

CLOTHING

Kids always make fun of me.
They laugh at my clothes,
Don't you see.
Holes in my pants,
Shirts too small,
Not a winter coat at all.
Kids always make fun of me.
Shoes too big,
Pants too small,
Holes in my socks,
Everything I need
I haven't got.
I can't run and hide;
I feel so bad inside.
Why do kids make fun of me?
I can't help the way I am.
Please don't make fun of me,
Don't you see?

QUESTIONS AND ACTIVITIES

1. How do you think the child in the poem feels?
    Explain your answer.

2. Why do you suppose this child doesn't have
    some of the things he needs?

3. If someone laughed at your clothes, how do you think you would feel?

4. Why do you suppose some children laugh
    and make fun of what others are wearing?

5. Can most students wear what they want to school? Explain.

6. What is the main idea of the poem?

7. In one sentence, write something you have learned from the poem.

FOR LITTLE BOYS ONLY

There's nothing like little girls.
They're the most precious things
In all the world.
If you do the right things,
They'll treat you like little kings.
Help them pick up
What they drop.
Say, "I'm sorry,"
"Excuse me,"
"Thank you," and "please."
Always share,
Then they'll know you really care.
If you treat them kindly
And don't cause them
Pain and trouble,
They'll give you sweetness
And kindness back double.
Do everything you can
To make them happy,
Even when you think
They're nuts and whacky.
Little girls want to be treated
Like pretty little queens.
But always remember,
There can never be
Pretty little queens
Without first having
Handsome little kings.

QUESTIONS AND ACTIVITIES

1. Who is the poet writing (talking) to? Should only boys read the poem?

2. Should boys treat all girls nicely or just the ones they like? Why?

3. Name some things boys can do to be nice to girls.

4. What will happen to the boys, if they treat the girls kindly?

5. How are kings and queens treated?

6. Would you like to be treated like a king or a queen?

7. What is the main idea of the poem?

8. In one sentence, write something you have learned from the poem.

9. Extra, draw an illustration from the poem.

FOR LITTLE GIRLS ONLY

There's nothing like a little boy.
He's rough, tough,
And a lot more stuff.
He's sometimes lazy,
Sometimes crazy,
But always mama's
Handsome sweet baby.
He's nice, kind,
And even sweet sometime.
He'll never admit it
To the rest of the world
That he's secretly in love
With you pretty little girls.
He'll pull your hair,
Just to let you know he's there.
He'll grab your book,
Just to make you take a look.
He'll cut in line,
Just so you'll be in front,
Or right behind.
He'll hit you and run.
Not to hurt you,
But hoping you'll chase
And touch him too.
He'll put you through
All of this,
Secretly hoping
For one little kiss.
All of the silly things
He'll ever do
Is his way of saying,
"I love you!"

QUESTIONS AND ACTIVITIES

1. Who is the poet writing (talking) to? Should only girls read the poem? Explain.

2. Do you think some boys act like the ones described in the poem? If so, why do you think they act that way?

3. If boys like girls, why don't they just tell them instead of doing all those things to get their attention?

4. What is the main idea of the poem?

5. In one sentence, write something you have learned from the poem.

DO YOU LOVE YOUR MOTHER?

Do you love your mother?
I don't think so, brother.
All she wants you to do
Is come to school,
Do the best you can,
And grow up to be
The right kind of man.
But all you do
Is refuse to work
And you play the part
Of a stupid jerk.
You come to school
Scream and shout
Like you have no idea
What love's all about.
Do you love your mother?
I don't think so, brother.
Every time you get in trouble
Your mother gets it back double.
So, next time you act
A fool in school,
Ask yourself one question.
Do I love my mother?
I don't think so, brother.

QUESTIONS AND ACTIVITIES

1. Do you love your mother?

2. How can you let your mother know that you love her?

3. What does "proud" mean?

4. Is it important to try to make your mother proud of you?

5. What kinds of things can you do in school to make your mother proud of you?

6. What can you do in school to make her feel bad or disappointed?

7. What do you think the author means by "every time you get in trouble, your mother gets it back double"? Do you agree with this?

8. What is the main idea of the poem?

9. In one sentence, write something you have learned from the poem.

I CAN DO MANY THINGS

Sittin' all alone
By this old oak tree.
None of the kids ever ask
To play with me.
I can't blame them though;
They think I can't do anything.
No, I can't climb a tree,
Can't jump rope,
Can't run,
But I can do things
That are fun.
I can play chess, video games,
Work puzzles, swim,
And I can work out
In the gym.
Wheelchair, wheelchair go away,
Come again some other day.
I can't run, skip, jump,
Or play on the swings,
But I can do many other things.

QUESTIONS AND ACTIVITIES

1. How does this person feel about herself?

2. How do you think other children feel about her?

3. Have you ever been physically unable to do things
   your friends could do because of illness or injury?
   If so, how did you feel?

4. How do you think you would feel, if the doctors told you
   that you were going to be permanently handicapped
   because of an injury or illness?

5. How do you think this girl could get other children to play with her?

6. If this girl lived in your neighborhood would you ask her to play with you? Explain your
   answer.

7. What is the main idea of the poem?

8. In one sentence, write something you have learned from the poem.

WHO AM I?

I'll make you lie.
I'll make you steal.
I'll make you lose weight
And your belly will ache.
I'll make you cuss your mama
And fight your dad.
I'll make you lose
Every friend you ever had.
And no matter how hard you try,
I'll make your sisters
And brothers weep and cry.
I'll make you rob a store,
Kill a stranger,
And I'll keep your youthful life in danger.
I won't let you eat
And I won't let you sleep.
I'll make you lose everything you own
And I'll never let you live
To be full grown.
I'll make you lose self-respect,
Confidence, faith, and hope.
Who Am I?
I'm Mr. Dope!

QUESTIONS AND ACTIVITIES

1. What is dope?

2. Is dope good for you? If so, how and if not,
   why are so many people using it?

3. What does the word "peer" mean?

4. What is peer pressure?

5. How do you think most people first start taking dope?

6. What would you do if you discovered that your brother,
   sister, or best friend was using dope?

7. How do you think we can get dope out of our schools
   and neighborhoods?

8. What is the main idea of the poem?

9. In one sentence, write something you have learned from the poem.

A NIGHTMARE

I had a terrible nightmare last night.
I woke up shaking,
As I turned on the light.
I dreamed I was living in a world
That I could not understand.
I was a frightened, helpless,
And confused man.
I could not understand any
Of the magazines, newspapers, or books.
I had no job, no money, and no security.
I was a very unhappy person indeed.
I was living in a civilized world
And I did not know how to read.

QUESTIONS AND ACTIVITIES

1. What is a nightmare?

2. What is the difference between a dream and a nightmare?

3. Have you ever had a nightmare? Share your experience with the class, if you like.

4. Explain the words security and civilized.

5. Name at least three things in this person's nightmare that were frightening to him.

6. What is the main idea of the poem?

7. In one sentence, write something you have learned from the poem.

8. Extra, draw an illustration from the poem.

RUNAWAYS

If you're having trouble at home
And you think you can't bear to stay,
The solution to your problem
Is not running away.
No matter how bad
Things seem at home,
It's ten times worse
In the streets alone.
Runaways are sleeping on the streets
And begging for food to eat.
They're doing things
They thought they'd never do.
And if you run away,
You might do these horrible things too.
They're robbing, stealing,
Selling themselves for a price,
And doing many other things
That are not very nice.
They're getting drunk, taking dope,
And losing hope.
Runaways stay frightened, confused,
And all alone,
And they wish every day
That they had never left home.
The streets are filled
With runaway kids
Who have nowhere to go
And nothing to do.
Don't let one of these kids be you.
I hope you think
About everything you've read;
Too many runaways end up dead!

QUESTIONS AND ACTIVITIES

1. Why do you think children run away from home?

2. Do you know anyone who ran away from home?
   If so, do you know what happened to him/her?

3. What are some of the terrible things runaways do?

4. What do you think most runaways wish?

5. Why does the author say you should never run away from home?

6. Have you ever left home? Have you ever thought about leaving home?
   Tell us why you left or why you thought about leaving.

7. If you are having serious problems at home, where can you go
   to get some help or advice.

8. What is the main idea of the poem?

9. In one sentence, write something you have learned from the poem.

THE OLDEST CHILD

My sisters and brothers
Are watching me.
They're watching everything I do,
And if you're the oldest child
In your family,
You're being watched closely too.
Your brothers and sisters
Are looking at everything you do,
And listening to everything you say.
So, you must be careful
About the way you live each day.
Your siblings are expecting you
To show them right from wrong
And to teach them good from bad.
You're a role model
In your household,
Just like your mom and dad.
Being the first born child
Is an honor and it's a chance
For you to lead the way.
So, always be careful
Of what you say and do.
When you're the oldest child
In the family,
Your siblings are watching you.

QUESTIONS AND ACTIVITIES

1. Explain the word sibling. (See the dictionary.)

2. Who is being watched in this poem?

3. Who is watching this person and why are they watching?

4. What is a role model? (See the dictionary.)

5. Do you think it is an honor to be the first born child in the family? Explain your answer.

6. Did you ever do or want to do something simply because your older brother or sister did it or was going to do it? Share your experience with the class, if you like.

7. In one sentence, write something you have learned from the poem.

8. What is the main idea of the poem?

9. Extra, draw an illustration from the poem.

KEEP OUR SCHOOLS CLEAN

The custodian is a busy man.
Help him out,
Whenever you can.
Keep our lavatories clean and neat.
When you come in from outside,
Always wipe your feet.
Never write on our nice clean walls,
And pick up any junk
You find in the halls.
Always flush the toilet,
Whenever you get through;
You know it's the only
Right thing to do.
Always check around your desk,
Before you leave the room.
Pick up whatever you see;
You don't need a brush or a broom.
Keeping our schools clean
Is an easy thing to do,
As long as we have helpers
Like me and you.

QUESTIONS AND ACTIVITIES

1. What is the name of your school custodian?

2. What is the custodian's job?

3. Why is it necessary to keep our schools clean?

4. Does a clean or dirty school have anything to do with learning? Explain your answer.

5. Why do you think students write on the walls?

6. Why do you think students deliberately dirty lavatories they have to use, too?

7. Why do you suppose some students do not flush the toilet when they have finished? If you see an unflushed toilet, what should you do?

8. Where should students first learn about cleanliness?

9. What is the main idea of the poem?

10. In one sentence, write something you have learned from the poem.

TOO MANY

There are ten screaming kids
In this small old house,
A mom, a dad,
And at least one mouse.
We have an even mixture
Of girls and boys,
But even when we're quiet,
We make a lot of noise.
The bedrooms are all crowded
And the kitchen's packed too.
I can't ever get in the bathroom
Whenever my time is due.
The radio's loud;
The TV is too.
The stereo's blastin'
And there's nothing I can do.
Can't find a place to study,
Or to think things out.
Sometimes I get so mad,
I just want out.
It looks like my situation
Will never come to an end.
Mom announced last night
She's pregnant again.

QUESTIONS AND ACTIVITIES

1. In your opinion, how many people are in a large family?

2. Do you live in a large family?

3. How many people live in your house?

4. Do you sometimes feel that your house is overcrowded like the person's house in the poem? If so, what can you do to help make life in your home better?

5. If your house is not a good place to study or to do homework, what other choices do you have?

6. Why does the person in the poem feel there is no end to his/her problem?

7. Would you rather grow up in a large or small family? Explain.

8. What is the main idea of the poem?

9. In one sentence, write something you have learned from the poem.

10. Extra, draw an illustration from the poem.

ALWAYS LET HER KNOW

My little sister
Is a pain in the neck.
She tells everything she knows
And she's always messing
With my clothes.
She wears my hats, shirts,
And even tries to wear my shoes.
She's nothing, but female bad news.
She ties up the phone all day,
Then eavesdrops on whatever
I have to say.
Mother thinks
She's a sweet little dear,
But I just wish
She'd evaporate or disappear.
But someday soon
We won't be together.
Maybe, we'll even be completely
Out of touch.
So, I'm going to tell her today
That I love her very much.

QUESTIONS AND ACTIVITIES

1. Explain the words "female," "eavesdrops," and "evaporate."

2. Do you have a brother or sister? If so, is he/she a "pain in the neck" sometimes? Explain your answer.

3. Have you ever said, "I love you" to your brother or sister?

4. If you love someone in your family, is it important to tell them? Explain your answer.

5. Why is the person in the poem going to tell his sister he loves her?

6. Does he really wish his sister would evaporate or disappear?

7. Why do you think his sister is always wearing his clothes?

8. What is the main idea of the poem?

9. In one sentence, write something you have learned from the poem.

10. Extra, draw an illustration from the poem.

STUTTERIN'

*One of the easiest things
In the world to do is talk.
For me, one of the hardest things
In the world to do is talk.
I know what I want to say,
But it just won't come out that way.
I stutter, stammer,
And fumble all about.
Kids laugh at me,
And make fun.
Why am I the only one?
I've tried everything,
But my speech stays the same.
Some comes out,
Some stays in,
And I have to start all over again.
Mom says not to worry;
I won't always be this way.
I hope I live long enough
To see that glorious day.*

QUESTIONS AND ACTIVITIES

1. What is stuttering?

2. What does the person in the poem have a hard time doing?

3. How does the person feel about his problem?

4. Why do you suppose some people laugh at people who stutter?

5. How do you think stutterers feel when people laugh at them and they're doing their very best to speak clearly?

6. Do you have a difficult time doing something that is easy for others to do? If so, tell about it.

7. Has anyone ever laughed at you when you were doing your best to do something that comes easily to others? If so, how did you feel?

8. What does the mother say about her child's problem? Do you agree with her? Explain.

9. Is there anything we can do to help people who stutter?

10. What is the main idea of the poem?

11. In one sentence, write something you have learned from the poem.

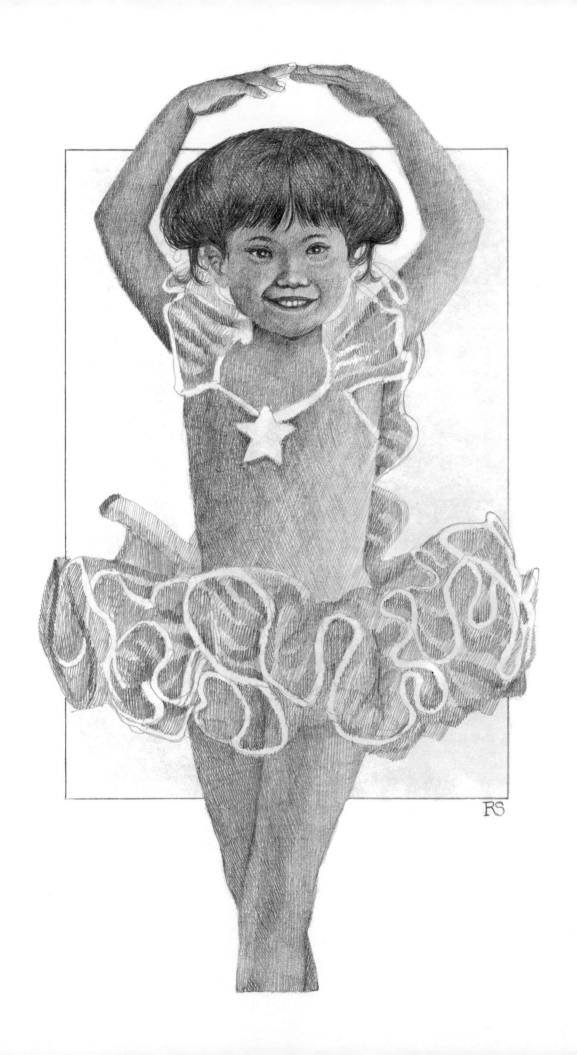

KEEP ON TRYING

Very few people succeed
At the first thing they do.
Many good people have failed
And you might too,
But keep on trying.
Sometimes life is rough
And the going gets tough.
Sometimes you'll shout
And just want out,
But keep on trying.
There is no doubt
Sometimes you'll strike out,
But that's what life is all about;
You keep on trying.
Life is not a piece of cake.
Everyone fails for goodness sakes,
But keep on trying.
The thing that separates
The people who do
From the people who don't
Is very very clear.
Those who don't,
Fail, cry, and never try again.
Those who do,
Fail, cry, but soon stop crying
And keep right on trying.

QUESTIONS AND ACTIVITIES

1. What does the author think is the difference between those who succeed and those who fail?

2. Is it a disgrace to fail? Explain.

3. Can any good ever come from a failing experience? Explain your answer.

4. Have you ever failed at something and later succeeded? Tell us about it.

5. Name a famous person who has succeeded at something. Do you think he or she was successful on the first try? If not, why do you think he/she finally succeeded.

6. What is the main idea of the poem?

7. In one sentence, write something you have learned from the poem.

CUSSING

Since the early age of three,
I've had cussing inside of me.
Whether I'm playing, working, or fussing,
I can't seem to stop cussing.
I've been punished, spanked,
And had my mouth washed
Out with soap.
No matter what my parents did,
They couldn't stop this cussing kid.
You so-and-so this,
You so-and-so that,
I even cuss
At my so-and-so hat.
Where did I get
Such a so-and-so mouth?
I got it inside
My so-and-so house.

QUESTIONS AND ACTIVITIES

1. When did the child start cussing?

2. What do you call an activity that is hard to stop?

3. Do you think this child has a "cussing" habit?
   If so, is it a good or bad habit?

4. Can you name something that is a good habit?

5. Where did this child learn how to cuss?

6. Should you be careful about what you say
   around smaller children? Why or why not?

7. What did the parents do to try to stop the child from cussing?

8. Why couldn't the parents stop the child from cussing?
   Do you think the child will ever stop?

9. What is the main idea of the poem?

10. In one sentence, write something you have learned from the poem.

THIS TIME BE SELFISH

Never let anyone use your comb
Or brush.
If you do,
You might find lice all over you.
They'll live in your hair
And you won't even know they're there.
First, you'll have one or two,
Then three, four,
And a hundred or more.
And no matter what you do,
They'll keep crawlin' all over you.
Anyone who has ever had them
Knows what they're all about,
And they'll surely tell you
It's very hard to get them out.
So, if you want your hair
To stay clean and fresh,
Never loan anyone your comb
Or brush.

QUESTIONS AND ACTIVITIES

1. What are lice?

2. What is a louse?

3. How do you think most people get lice?

4. Is it easy to remove lice from your hair?

5. How can you get rid of lice?

6. Is it alright to loan someone your comb, brush, or hat?

7. Is it alright to loan your best friends you comb, brush, or hat?

8. If someone wanted to borrow your comb, brush, or hat how could you refuse them without hurting their feelings?

9. What is the main idea of the poem?

10. In one sentence, write something you have learned from the poem.

DAD IS MY BEST FRIEND

There is no one in the world
Like my dad.
He's been raising me
As a single parent
Since I was three,
And he means everything to me.
We're a family of two.
I don't have a mother,
Brother, or sister.
But thanks to my dad,
He's the best friend I ever had.
He takes good care
Of me each day,
And he treats me in a special way.
I ride his back like a potato sack.
He swings me around
Like a merry-go-round.
If I'm feeling bad
And I start to cry,
He'll wipe the tear
Right out of my eye.
I can sit on his lap and talk,
Or sit on his lap and take a nap.
He rides me around in his car,
And treats me like a movie star.
But the best of all
Is when he reads to me
While I'm in bed,
And lets me rub the bald spot
In the middle of his head.

QUESTIONS AND ACTIVITIES

1. How does this boy feel about his dad? Explain your answer.

2. What is a single parent?

3. Name three things this child's dad does for him that he likes.

4. When he is with his dad, what does he like to do best of all?

5. What do you like best about your dad, grandfather, uncle, or special male adult in your life?

6. Do you think daddies are the best friends? Explain your answer.

7. What is the main idea of the poem?

8. Extra, draw an illustration from the poem.

NEW STUDENT

If a new student comes
Into your room today,
Treat him or her
In a special way.
Do everything you can do
To make them feel
Comfortable too.
Go up to them right away;
Have something nice
And kind to say.
There's nothing like
A friendly Joe,
When you're in a room full
Of people that you don't know.
So, whenever you see
A brand new face,
Be careful what you say
And do.
You never know
How life works out;
The next one might be you.

QUESTIONS AND ACTIVITIES

1. Have you ever gone to a new school?

2. How did you feel on the first day?

3. Did anyone do or say something to make you feel comfortable? Tell about your experience.

4. Did anyone do or say something to make you feel uncomfortable? Tell us about it.

5. If a new student came into our classroom, what would you do or say to make the person feel welcome?

6. What is a "friendly Joe"?

7. Explain the last three lines of the poem.

8. What is the main idea of the poem?

9. In one sentence, write something you have learned from the poem.

10. Extra, draw an illustration from the poem.

BLACK BLACK

I am black.
Not just black,
I'm black black.
I'm the blackest person
I have ever seen.
I must be the blackest person
Others have ever seen too.
Otherwise, they wouldn't stare
At me like they do.
White kids call me black.
Even black kids call me black,
But they don't upset me.
I feel good about myself,
'Cause black is beautiful.
So, if I'm the blackest person
In the world,
That makes me
One of the most beautiful human beings
On earth.

QUESTIONS AND ACTIVITIES

1. How does the person feel about herself?
   Why does she feel this way?

2. How do you feel about yourself?

3. Is it important to feel good about yourself?
   Explain your answer.

4. Is it better to be black, white, red, brown, or yellow?
   Explain.

5. Has anyone ever called you "black"? If so, how did you feel?
   Why do you suppose you felt that way?

6. Have you ever called anyone "black"? If so, how did you feel?
   How do you think the person felt?

7. Many people say black is beautiful. Is black really beautiful?
   Explain.

8. What does it mean to "stare"? Should you stare at people?
   Explain.

9. What is the main idea of the poem?

10. In one sentence, write something you have learned from the poem.

A GOOD SPORT

All games should be fun
Whether you win or whether you lose.
No one in the game
Should walk away with the blues.
Winning is great.
It makes you feel fine,
But there's really no fun
In winning all the time.
Whenever you lose,
Shake the winners' hands.
Let them know
That you've done all that you can.
They had everything their way today,
But maybe you'll win next time
When you meet for a replay.
Whenever you win
Shake the losers' hands.
Let them know
That you care and understand.
Being a good sport
Is the only way to go.
It's the first step on the ladder
Toward becoming a pro.

QUESTIONS AND ACTIVITIES

1. What does it mean to have the "blues"?

2. Is it fun to win all the time? Explain your answer.

3. Why do people shake hands after a game or a match?

4. What does it mean to be a "good sport"?

5. Why do boys and girls play games?

6. What is a "pro"?

7. What is the main idea of the poem?

8. In one sentence, write something you have learned from the poem.

9. Extra, draw an illustration from the poem.

I WONDER

I wonder where
I can find a friend?
I wonder where
There are people who care?
I wonder where
I can speak what's on my mind?
I wonder where
I can get understanding anytime?
I wonder where
I can find happiness and love?
I wonder where
I can be myself and no one else?
I wonder where
I can learn anything I want?
I wonder where
Everyone is treated the same?
I wonder where I can succeed?
I wonder where
Failure always means a second chance?
I wonder where
I can learn
And practice The Golden Rule?
I can find all of this,
If I only stay in school.

QUESTIONS AND ACTIVITIES

1. Why is it important to stay in school at least until you graduate from high school?

2. Do you know anyone who has dropped out of school?
   If so, what is he/she doing now?

3. Why do you think some students drop out of school?

4. What do you like best about school?

5. What do you dislike about school?

6. What is "The Golden Rule"?

7. Can you name something else you can find in school
   that was not mentioned in the poem?

8. Many people say the years you spend in school are the
   best years of your life. Do you agree with this statement?
   Explain your answer.

9. What is the main idea of the poem?

10. In one sentence, write something you have learned from the poem.

11. Extra, draw an illustration from the poem.

I DARE YOU

I dare you
To jump off that barn.
I jumped.
To walk that narrow fence.
I walked.
To jump over that ditch.
Over I went.
To catch that bee.
It's in my hand.
To climb that tree.
I'm at the top.
To break that bottle.
It's broken.
To ride on the back of that truck.
I slipped!
Never take a dangerous dare,
Whatever you ever do.
If you take a dangerous dare,
That might be the end of you.

QUESTIONS AND ACTIVITIES

1. What is a dare?

2. Have you ever done something that someone dared you to do? Tell about it.

3. Have you ever dared someone to do something? If so, tell about it.

4. Why do you suppose people take dares?

5. Is it alright to take a dare? Explain.

6. Is it ever wrong to take a dare?

7. What finally happened to the person in the poem?

8. What is the main idea of the poem?

9. In one sentence, write something you have learned from the poem.

10. Extra, draw an illustration from the poem.

OVERWEIGHT

I look in the mirror
Every day and every night,
Trying to convince myself
That I look alright.
But here I stand,
Overweight since I was four
And instead of losing weight,
I'm constantly gaining more.
I diet, exercise,
And do everything I can
To lose weight,
But nothing seems to work;
It must be my fate.
I don't know what else to do.
If I just look at food,
I seem to gain a pound or two.
Mother says it's only baby fat
And I wouldn't always look like that.
I certainly hope she is right.
Someone called me fat again last night.

QUESTIONS AND ACTIVITIES

1. How does the person feel about being overweight?

2. How do you think most people become overweight?

3. What has the person done to lose weight?

4. What is dieting and can it be dangerous to your health?

5. Write the meaning of the word fate.

6. Is there anything else this person could do to lose weight?

7. Should you laugh or make fun of people who are overweight? Explain.

8. Is there anything wrong with being overweight?

9. What did mother say about her child's overweight condition? Do you agree?

10. In one sentence, write something you have learned from the poem.

11. What is the main idea of the poem?

I OUGHT TO

I ought to
Do more things for my
Sister and brother.
I ought to
Help mother with all this work.
I ought to
Be more respectful to adults.
I ought to
Stop asking for so much money.
I ought to
Do better in school.
I ought to
Keep my room clean.
I ought to
Stop talking about people.
I ought to
Be proud of who I am.
I ought to
Stop talking back to teachers.
I ought to
Spend more time
With my grandparents.
I ought to
Write to my relatives sometime.
I ought to
Tell mom and dad I love them.
I ought to
Do all of these things
And I ought to
Start right now!

QUESTIONS AND ACTIVITIES

1. What is a procrastinator?

2. Do you think the person in the poem is a procrastinator?
   Why or why not?

3. Do you ever "put off" doing things you feel you should be doing?
   What are some of those things?

4. There are many things mentioned in the poem that the person says she ought
   to do. Name some of the things you ought to do that you haven't done.

5. In your opinion, which one of the things mentioned in the poem
   is the most important thing you ought to do? Why?

6. What is the main idea of the poem?

7. In one sentence, write something you have learned from the poem.

8. Extra, draw an illustration from the poem.

AS GOOD AS ANYONE

Never feel unworthy,
If you're on welfare
Or A.D.C.
Sometimes in life,
That's the way it has to be.
Everyone in this world
Has accepted a helping hand.
When you're on public assistance,
Good people understand.
So, hold your head up high
And get important things done.
Sure, you're on public assistance,
But you're as good as anyone.
The time will come
When you'll have your chance to give.
Helping people out
Is the only way to live.

QUESTIONS AND ACTIVITIES

1. Explain the terms "welfare," "A.D.C.," and "public assistance."

2. What does "unworthy" mean?

3. Why might some people feel unworthy, if they are on public assistance?

4. If you're on public assistance, how should you feel? Why?

5. Everyone has not been on public assistance, but do you think everyone has accepted some kind of help at sometime or another? Explain.

6. If you're on public assistance, what did the author say you should do?

7. What is the main idea of the poem?

8. In one sentence, write something you have learned from the poem.

WHERE'S MY TEETH?

Sliding down the bannister,
What a thrilling ride.
Zip, zap, zoom,
What a breath-taking slide.
Can't help doing it;
I do it every day.
Wish those dumb kids
Would get the heck
Out of my way.
Teachers have warned me
And the principal has too,
But I'm never stopping
What I like to do.
Zip, zap, zoom,
I'm not doing it anymore.
I landed smack on my face today;
Two teeth on the stupid floor!

QUESTIONS AND ACTIVITIES

1. Have you ever slid down a bannister in school?

2. Why do kids do it?

3. Why do you think it is forbidden in school?

4. Do you think the person in the poem will slide down another bannister? Why or why not?

5. What is the worst thing that could happen to you, if you slid down a bannister?

6. What is the main idea of the poem?

7. In one sentence, write something you have learned from the poem.

NEW CLOTHES

From my head to my toes
I've got on brand new clothes.
I've been in the mirror all night,
Can't wait till the morning light.
I feel good all inside;
Must be that thing called pride.
I've never been like this before.
Can't wait to open that school door.
I want all my friends
And classmates to see.
But most of all,
I hope my teacher notices me.

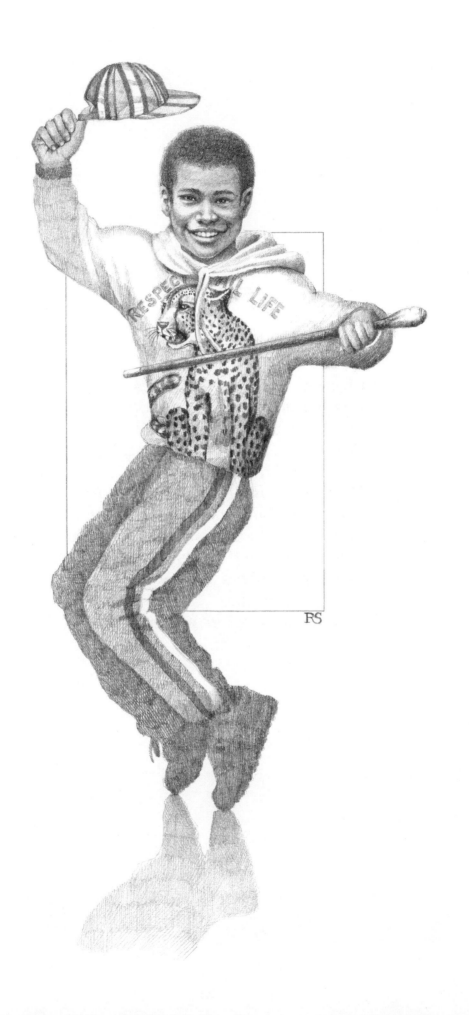

QUESTIONS AND ACTIVITIES

1. How does the child in the poem feel?

2. Why does he feel that way?

3. What is pride?

4. Is it important that people have pride? Explain.

5. Who does this person want to see him in his new clothes?

6. How do you think this student feels about his teacher?

7. What is the main idea of the poem?

8. In one sentence, write something you have learned from this poem.

9. Extra, draw an illustration from the poem.

TOO TALL

Tall as a telephone pole,
Limbs like a tree.
There's no student
In the school as tall as me.
String bean, legs, bones,
And stick they call me.
I hear high pockets,
Mountain, steeple, and door.
I feel so bad,
I can't stand it anymore.
They think it's alright
'Cause they're just
Playing games.
Wish they could really see
How much pain they're causing me.
Taller than all the boys,
Taller than all the girls.
Soon I'll be in the tree
With the squirrels.
Why do they make fun
Of me like they do?
I need kindness
And understanding too.
How long do I have to live
With all this pain and strife?
Guess I'll have to bear it
For the rest of my life.

QUESTIONS AND ACTIVITIES

1. How does this student feel?

2. Why does he feel this way?

3. What names do the other students call this person?

4. Why do you think they call this student names?

5. Do you think the name callers realize they are hurting this student's feelings when they call those names?

6. Have you ever called anyone any of those names? If so, would you do it again? Explain.

7. Do you have a nickname you don't like? If so, how do you feel when people call you by that nickname?

8. When does the student in the poem think his problem will end?

9. If you knew the student in the poem, what could you do to help him?

10. What is the main idea of the poem?

11. In one sentence, write something you have learned from the poem.

12. Extra, draw an illustration from the poem.

HATE

Why do people hate?
They hate for many reasons
I'm very sad to say,
But it doesn't always
Have to be this way.
Hate has been
In this world too long,
And everyone knows hate is wrong.
Adults not only have failed
To eliminate hate
From our society,
Hate is steadily on the rise.
And if we don't do something soon,
It will lead to our own demise.
It's time for us
To destroy this monster
Once and for all;
That's why I'm giving
All young people a call.
I'm asking each of you
To do your part
And to never let hate
Enter your heart.
Always choose love over hate
And right over wrong.
If we are to eliminate hate
From this world,
We must start
With every young boy and girl.

QUESTIONS AND ACTIVITIES

1. Why do people hate? List as many reasons as you can.

2. Do you think hate is wrong? Explain your answer.

3. The poet says hate is on the rise. Do you agree with this statement? If so, what do you think is the reason for this?

4. What can you do to help eliminate hate from our society?

5. What is the meaning of the word monster? (See the dictionary.)

6. What does the word monster refer to in this poem?

7. Who is the poet asking to stop hate in the world?

8. In one sentence, write something you have learned from the poem.

9. What is the main idea of the poem?

I LOVE MY GLASSES

Some teachers wear glasses,
Some principals do too.
I wear glasses,
What about you?
Glasses are worn all over the world,
By all kinds of boys
And by all kinds of girls.
When my glasses are on my face,
I can see all over the place.
I can see things up close
And things far away.
So, I put my glasses on every single day.
Now, I can see better,
I look better, And believe it or not,
My grades are getting better.
Last night,
My cat was in bed with me
And we both fell asleep
Watching my color TV.
When I woke up this morning,
I looked in the bed,
Under the bed,
On the floor,
And everywhere,
But I couldn't find my glasses anywhere.
Finally, I went into the bathroom,
And I happened to look in the mirror.
And much to my surprise,
There were my beautiful glasses
Right there on my beautiful eyes.

QUESTIONS AND ACTIVTIES

1. What kinds of people wear glasses?

2. Why do people wear glasses?

3. Do you wear glasses? If so, how do you feel about wearing them?

4. Does anyone in your family wear glasses? If so, do you know how they feel about wearing glasses?

5. Some people wear glasses who don't need them. Why do you think they do this?

6. Explain the terms vision, nearsighted, and farsighted.

7. What are contact lenses?

8. What are some of the advantages and disadvantages of wearing contact lenses?

9. If you had to improve you vision, would you prefer to wear glasses or contact lenses? Explain your answer.

10. What is the main idea of the poem?

11. In one sentence, write something you have learned from the poem.

12. Extra, draw an illustration about the poem.

I'M FROM THE MIDDLE EAST

My name is Ali Rasaad,
And I'm from the Middle East.
My family migrated to America
A few years ago
Seeking work, happiness, and peace.
We are proud of our people,
Our language, and our heritage too,
And we are doing our best
To be friends with you.
All we want to do is to live
And grow in this great land,
But we need you
And other good Americans to understand,
And to lend us a helping hand.
We eat different kinds
Of food sometimes,
We dress differently sometimes,
And we talk differently sometimes,
But we are good loyal Americans
All of the time.

QUESTIONS AND ACTIVITIES

1. Locate the area called the Middle East on a world map or globe and list at least three Middle Eastern countries. (More if you can.) Your teacher will assist you.

2. Write the meaning of the word migrate.

3. Write the meaning of the word heritage.

4. Why did Ali Rasaad and his family come to America?

5. What does Ali want you and other good Americans to do?

6. If a new student from the Middle East or from any other country enrolled into your classroom or school, what should you do to make the student feel welcome?

7. Do you think we should allow people from other countries to come to America to live? Explain your answer.

8. If you had the opportunity to live in another country for a year, which country would you choose and why?

9. In one sentence, write something you have learned from the poem.

10. What is the main idea of the poem?

STEALING

Never take anything
That belongs to someone else.
No matter how badly you want something,
Or how deprived you might feel,
There is no good reason
For you to steal.
You can't always get
What you want when you want it.
But if you prepare yourself in school
And work hard each day,
Soon you'll get what you want;
That's the American way.
All over the world,
Stealing is a crime
And sooner or later
Thieves go to jail to do some time.
Always remember,
When you take something
That belongs to someone else,
You take a little something
Away from yourself.

QUESTIONS AND ACTIVITIES

1. Do you think stealing is wrong? Explain your answer.

2. Is there ever a time when stealing is alright?
   If so, when is stealing justified? (alright)

3. Have you ever had the urge to steal anything?
   If so, tell us about it if you like.

4. What is the meaning of the word deprived in line four?

5. What does the author mean when he says, "That's the American way"?

6. Do you think some people steal more than others?
   Explain your answer.

7. Some people go to jail for stealing. What else might
   happen to a person who is caught stealing?

8. Explain the last four lines of the poem.

9. What is the main idea of the poem?

10. Extra, draw an illustration from the poem.

TEACHERS MAKE MISTAKES TOO

Sometimes kids get mad
At their parents
Because they can't have their way,
But their anger doesn't last
Longer than a day.
Sometimes students get mad
At their teachers
Because they can't have their way,
But sometimes their anger lasts
Longer than a day.
Sometimes students get mad
At their teachers
And stay mad for a week, for a month,
And sometimes all year long,
And this is wrong!
Teachers are human beings too.
Sometimes they make mistakes
Just like your parents
And blame you for something
That you didn't do.
If this ever happens to you,
Be understanding and go on your way,
But never let your anger last
Longer than a day.

QUESTIONS AND ACTIVITIES

1. Have you ever gotten mad at your parents?
   If so, please tell us about it, if you like.
   How long did your anger last?

2. Have you ever gotten mad at a teacher? If so, tell us about it, if you like.
   How long did your anger last?

3. Were you ever blamed for something you didn't do? If so, did you get angry?
   Tell us about your experience, if you like.

4. What is the main idea of the poem?

5. In one sentence, write one thing you have learned from the poem.

6. Extra, draw an illustration from the poem.

NEVER POINT

Never point your finger.
It's not a nice thing to do.
If you don't point
Your finger at me,
I won't point mine at you.
A traffic sign points,
A special breed
Of dog points,
And a needle points too.
It's okay for some things
To point,
But not for me and you,
Lots of people point,
But they know it's
The wrong thing to do.
But intelligent people never point
And that's my point of view.

QUESTIONS AND ACTIVITIES

1. Is it wrong to point your finger?

2. When is it wrong to point?

3. Is it ever right to point? Explain.

4. What is the main idea of the poem?

5. In one sentence, write something you have learned from the poem.

DANGEROUS WEAPONS

Never bring a weapon to school.
Always obey this important rule.
You can't solve your problems
With a gun or a knife
And you don't have the right
To threaten anyone's life.
If someone in school
Is threatening you,
Tell the people in charge
And they will gladly help you.
There is nothing macho
In carrying a gun.
It's a stupid situation for anyone.
The killing of a human being
Is a terrible thing to see.
It's not painless and bloodless
Like you see on TV.
If you maim someone,
You will live a life of regret
And if you kill someone,
You will never forget!

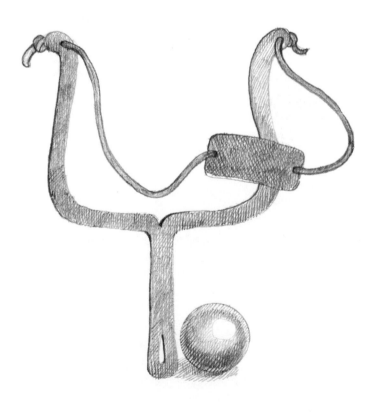

QUESTIONS AND ACTIVITIES

1. What is a weapon?

2. What does "macho" mean?

3. Do you think being "macho" has anything to do with students carrying weapons to school?

4. Give some other reasons why you think students bring weapons into our schools.

5. What does it mean to maim someone?

6. What should you do, if you are having problems with another student?

7. If you saw a gun or a knife in a good friend's locker, what would you do?

8. Name three things that are violations of the "Student Code of Conduct."

9. What is the main idea of the poem?

10. In one sentence, write something you have learned from the poem.

SHORTY

Everyone around me
Is looking over my head.
Why did I have to be so small
And everyone else so tall?
"Hi, Shorty."
"See you later, Shorty"
I hear it every day.
Seems that they
Would respect my feelings
And have kinder words to say.
Shrimp, shorty, pee wee,
I hear it all the time.
I think about their feelings;
Why don't they think about mine?
I know I'm short,
And they too can see.
So, why do they call me shorty
And keep reminding me?

QUESTIONS AND ACTIVITIES

1. Does this person feel good about himself? Explain.

2. What names do the children call him?

3. Why do they call him those names?

4. What does the term "standard of beauty" mean?

5. Explain the words inferior and superior.

6. Are taller people superior and shorter people inferior? Explain.

7. If you think a person is tall or short, is this a fact or an opinion?

8. If you had a choice, would you rather be tall or short? Explain.

9. Does a person's height have anything to do with failure or happiness in life?

10. Is there anything about yourself that you would like to change, if you could? Tell us about it.

11. What is the main idea of the poem?

12. In one sentence, write something you have learned from the poem.

ALWAYS LET HIM KNOW

I'd love to have a sister,
But all I have is
A big dumb brother.
He calls me names,
He pulls my hair,
And he leaves his clothes
Laying everywhere.
He plays his radio too loud,
Never wants to take a bath,
Eats like a pig,
And thinks he's Mr. Big.
I can't wait for him
To go away to school.
Then, I'd be rid
Of that crazy fool.
He's as nutty as can be
And he's always making fun of me,
But he's my handsome big brother
And I know
We'll always love each other.
So, I'm going to do it right away
And tell that fool
I love him today.

QUESTIONS AND ACTIVITIES

1. Do you have a brother? If so, how does he treat you? How do you treat him?

2. Why does the person in the poem want her brother to go away to school?

3. How does she really feel about her brother? Do you think she really wants him to go away? Explain.

4. How do you think the brother feels about her?

5. If you love someone in your family, is it important that you tell them? Why?

6. How can you express your love for your relatives in other ways?

7. What is the main idea of the poem?

8. In one sentence, write something you have learned from the poem.

9. Extra, draw an illustration from the poem.

BUSSING

We're riding by a school we love.
They're bussing us clear across town.
They're bussing Me, Billy, Sally, and Sue.
I'll even bet they're bussing you.
Mother is mad.
Father is too.
Our friends and neighbors
Are all feeling blue.
Bussing has us all uptight.
Is it wrong,
Or is it right?
But maybe,
Bussing won't be so bad.
Our new school might be
The best school we ever had.
I'll think positive thoughts
And just patiently wait and see.
Why don't you be smart
And do exactly like me?

QUESTIONS AND ACTIVITIES

1. What does "bussing" mean?

2. Why do we have bussing?

3. Do you think bussing is good or bad? What is good about it? What is bad about it?

4. Why do you think the mother and father in the poem are upset?

5. What does the word "positive" mean in the poem?

6. Do you ride the bus to this school? If so, how did you feel the first time you learned you were going to be bussed here?

7. If you had to be bussed to a different school, would you have those same feelings, or would you feel differently?

8. If you had a choice, would you rather be bussed to school, or walk to a school near your home? Why?

9. What is the main idea of the poem?

10. In one sentence, write something you have learned from the poem.

11. Extra, draw an illustration from the poem.

SKIPPING SCHOOL

I skipped school the other day.
I thought I'd go
To the arcade to play.
I played the videos
For quite a long time.
Finally, I spent my very last dime.
I started to walk
Out the front door,
But the next thing I knew
I was flat on the floor.
Some strange boys beat me so bad
I could hardly see.
Why did they want to bother me?
Did I say something they didn't like?
Did they think I had money?
Why they beat me,
I don't know.
But if I had been
Where I was supposed to be,
This crazy thing
Would never have happened to me.

QUESTIONS AND ACTIVITIES

1. Why did this student skip school?

2. What happened to the student when he or she started to leave the arcade?

3. Why do you think the strange boys did this terrible thing to this student?

4. Explain the last four lines of the poem.

5. Do you think this student will ever skip school again? Explain your answer.

6. Have you ever skipped school? If so, tell about it.

7. Give three good reasons why you should never skip school.

8. What is the main idea of the poem?

9. In one sentence, write something you have learned from the poem.

10. Extra, draw an illustration from the poem.

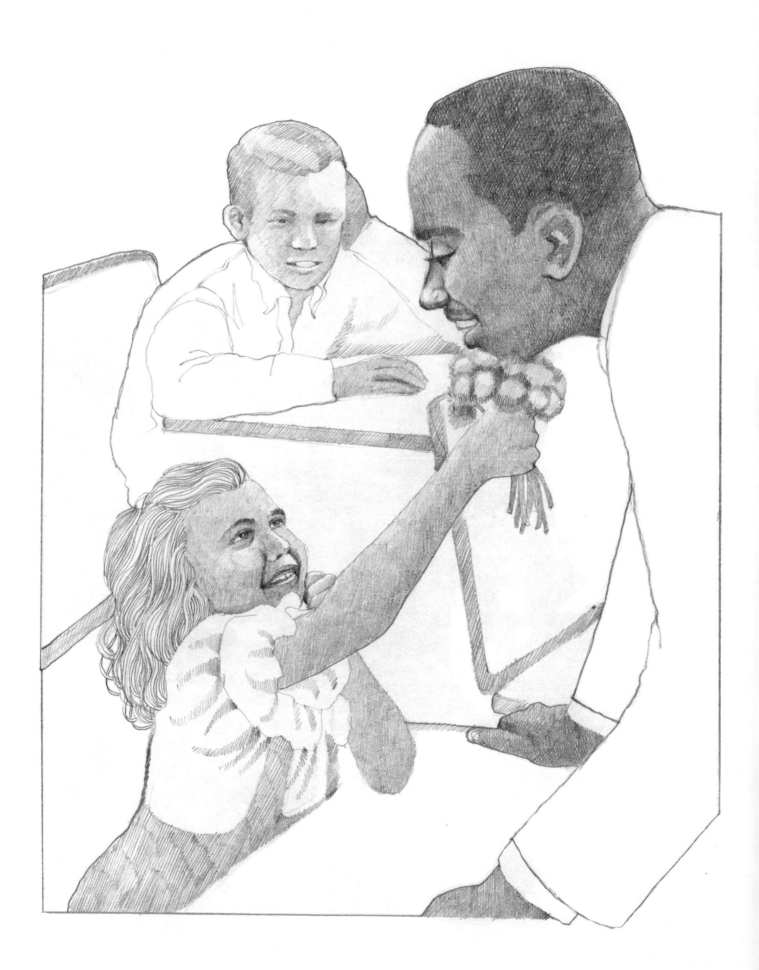

THE BEST

What is the most important profession
In the world?
Doctors, lawyers, engineers, you say.
Where would they be,
If you took the teachers away?
Teachers have to be
Doctors, lawyers, and engineers too.
They're mothers, fathers,
And I'm not through.
They're therapists, judges,
And accountants galore.
They have to be,
Whatever a child's asking for.
They do so many things that have
To be done;
They've touched the lives
Of everyone.
The world could survive
Without doctors, lawyers, engineers,
And preachers.
But what kind of world
Would it be,
Without our dedicated teachers?

QUESTIONS AND ACTIVITIES

1. What is a "profession"?

2. What is the difference between a "profession" and a "job"?

3. What does the author think is the most important profession? Do you agree? If not, what do you think?

4. There are signs and bumper stickers that read, "If you can read this, thank a teacher." What does this mean to you?

5. When you are older, what kind of work would you like to do?

6. Do you know how much education you will need for this kind of work?

7. What does the author mean when he states that teachers have to be mothers, fathers, doctors, lawyers, etc.?

8. What does "dedicated" mean?

9. What is the main idea of the poem?

10. In one sentence, write something you have learned from the poem.

11. Extra, draw an illustration from the poem.

JOHNNY COULDN'T READ

Johnny couldn't read.
He wouldn't even try.
As soon as he was old enough,
He bade his school good-bye.
"I can walk, talk, work,
And see," said he.
"And that's enough schooling for me."
"Besides, I know plenty of guys
Who read all the time,
And they don't have
A cotton pickin' dime."
Well, Johnny died last year.
But if he had learned how to read,
He'd still be here.
He died sometime last winter.
He walked right past a sign that read:
DANGER DO NOT ENTER!

QUESTIONS AND ACTIVITIES

1. Why do you think Johnny couldn't read?

2. Why did he quit school?

3. How old do you think Johnny was when he quit school?

4. Do you know anyone who has quit school before graduating from high school? If so, what is he/she doing now?

5. When and how did Johnny die?

6. Do you think his death could have been avoided? If so, how?

7. There are millions of people in the world who cannot read or write. What do you think is the reason for this tragedy?

8. What does the word illiterate mean?

9. A famous author said the worst thing that could happen to a person is being illiterate. The author said it was worse than being blind, deaf, or any other physical handicap. Do you agree with the author? Explain your answer.

10. What is the main idea of the poem?

11. In one sentence, write something you have learned from the poem.

12. Extra, draw an illustration from the poem.

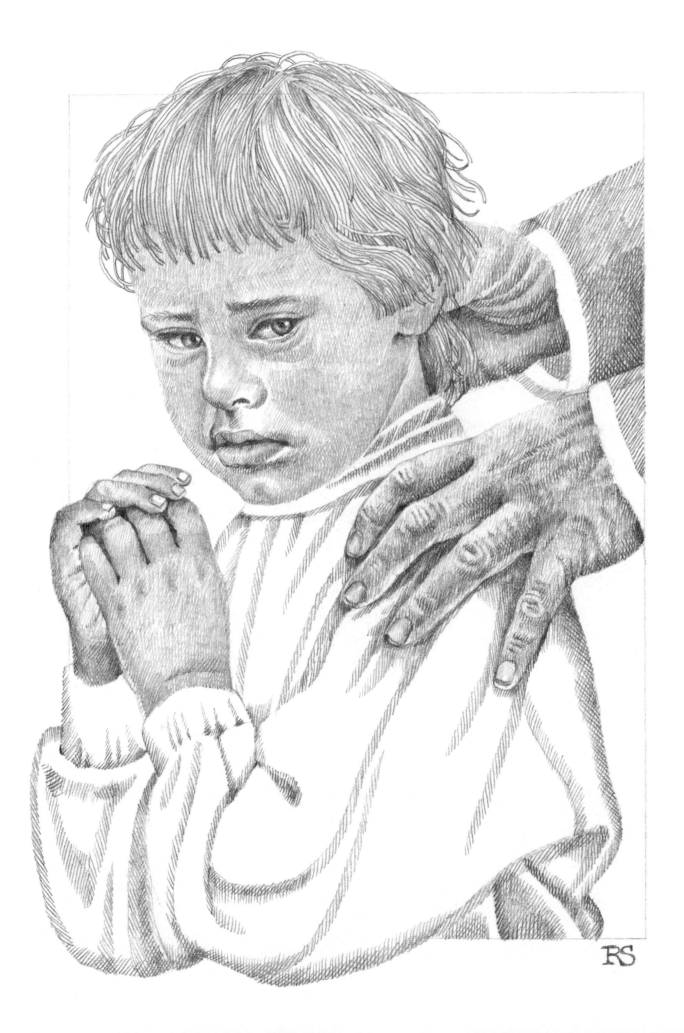

STRANGERS

Never walk by yourself;
Always walk with someone else.
Never talk to strangers;
It's not the thing to do.
Don't talk to them;
Don't let them talk to you.
If they start to talk to you,
Keep walking on your way.
Don't stop to speak with them
No matter what they say.
If they start to follow you,
Run as fast as you can.
Yell and scream very loud
'Till you draw a friendly crowd.
Then run to any place
You think might be safe.
Everyone unknown to you
Is not a threat of danger,
But always be cautious, alert,
And ready,
Whenever you meet a stranger.

QUESTIONS AND ACTIVITIES

1. Should you walk to and from school by yourself or always try to walk with someone else? Why?

2. Who is a stranger?

3. Should you ever stop and talk to a stranger?

4. Is it alright to talk to a stranger, if the stranger is a teenager or a woman? Explain.

5. What should you do, if you are chased by a stranger?

6. Explain the words cautious and alert.

7. Should you be afraid of every stranger you meet? Explain.

8. Should you be cautious and alert whenever you meet any stranger? Explain.

9. What is the main idea of the poem?

10. In one sentence, write something you have learned from the poem.

11. Extra, draw an illustration from the poem.

HOMEWORK

I didn't do my homework last night;
Too busy watching TV
With my brother Jeff.
Must tell the teacher something,
I can't afford to get another F.
Maybe, I'll say I lost it
On the way to school.
Better not say that;
My teacher's no fool.
I'll say my baby brother
Tore it up.
Better change my mind;
I said that last time.
I'll say I had to go
To the dentist.
Can't go that way;
I said that the other day.
I'll say my house caught on fire;
Then she'll know
I'm a great big liar.
My goodness, what a jerk!
Trying to think up
All these excuses
Is harder than doing my homework.

QUESTIONS AND ACTIVITIES

1. Why do teachers give homework?

2. If you have difficulty with your homework, what should you do?

3. Is the place where you do your homework important? Explain your answer.

4. Have you ever made up an excuse for not doing your homework? What excuse did you give? Tell about your situation.

5. What can you do to make sure you will not forget to bring your homework to school?

6. Why does the person in the poem think she is a "jerk"?

7. What is the main idea of the poem?

8. In one sentence, write something you have learned from the poem.

9. Extra, draw an illustration from the poem.

CHILD ABUSE

Child abuse is nothing new.
It could have happened to me
And it could be happening to you.
It is hurting a child in some cruel way.
It could be severe beating with a belt,
A hit with a stick,
A kick in the back,
A slap in the face,
Or a gentle touch in a private place.
If things like these ever happen to you,
Please, let someone know.
Child abuse can be caused
By your father, mother, sister, or brother.
By your uncle, aunt, a perfect stranger,
Or someone you know so very very well.
And if it ever happens to you,
It's your obligation and right
To go and tell.
You can tell your school principal,
Counselor, teacher, minister,
Or anyone you think you can trust,
But telling someone is always a must.
If child abuse ever happens to you,
Tell someone right away.
Never hesitate and wait too long
Because child abuse is always wrong!

QUESTIONS AND ACTIVITIES

1. What is child abuse?

2. Who might be a child abuser?

3. Is child abuse only happening in our city, or is it happening in other places too?

4. Does it happen among rich families or poor families?

5. Does it happen in all communities or does it happen only to certain racial groups?

6. How old does a child have to be to experience child abuse?

7. If you are being abused by someone, what should you do?

8. If you know of a child who is being abused by someone, what should you do?

9. What is the main idea of the poem?

10. In one sentence, write something you have learned from the poem.

SMOKING

I'm up here in the eighth grade
And I have a few regrets.
Two months before I was nine years old,
I started smoking cigarettes.
Ma smokes, Pa smoked,
And so did Uncle Frank and Aunt Sue.
Sister smokes, brother smokes
And some of my friends are smoking too.
But smoking will give you
Heart attacks, cancer, strokes,
And it will shorten your living days.
Uncle Frank lived a very short life
And so did his young
And beautiful wife.
Uncle Frank died at the young age of 34
And his young beautiful wife
Lived only two years more.
Pa lived a short life too,
He died at the age of 42.
Cigarettes are silent killers,
But they have some faults that can be seen.
They make your breath smell very bad
And they turn your teeth all green.
Some people say cigarette smoking
Will never cause you to die,
But that's the profiteers' great big lie.
Cigarettes have been killing people
For years and years.
They've caused too many funerals
And too many tears.
Don't ever start to smoke,
It's a deadly thing to do.
I'm glad I had the courage to quit
And if I can quit, others can too.
If you are smoking now,
Do everything you can to stop
And don't ever lose hope.
Don't let your life go up in smoke!

QUESTIONS AND ACTIVITIES

1. How old was this boy when he started smoking?

2. Why do you think he started smoking?

3. Why do you think most smokers start smoking?

4. What will smoking do to you?

5. How long do you think the average person can expect to live?

6. Do non-smokers live longer than smokers? If so, how much longer do you think?

7. What is a profiteer? (See dictionary.)

8. Is it hard for a person who has smoked for years to stop? Explain your answer.

9. On airplanes, in restaurants, in schools, and in many other places people are not allowed to smoke in certain sections, and in some places there is no smoking at all. Why do you think these new rules have been put into operation?

10. Why do you think this young boy quit smoking?

11. In one sentence, write something you have learned from the poem.

12. What is the main idea of the poem?

MOTHER'S DAY

Mother's Day is coming soon,
And I don't have a dime.
I want to buy her
Something nice,
But I stay broke
All the time.
I'd like to buy her
A brand new dress,
Or something she could wear.
Maybe something for her room;
A rug, a table, or a chair.
Since I can't give her
Any of this,
I'll just give her
A great big kiss.
"I love you mother!"
"Happy Mother's Day!"

QUESTIONS AND ACTIVITIES

1. In what month is Mother's Day?

2. What is the purpose of Mother's Day?

3. Why didn't the person in this poem buy his mother a gift?

4. Is it necessary that you buy your mother a gift on Mother's Day? Explain.

5. Besides buying a gift, what else can you do to show you love your mother on Mother's Day?

6. Do you think the child in the poem made his mother happy? Explain your answer.

7. What is the main idea of the poem?

8. In one sentence, write something you have learned from the poem.

9. Extra, draw an illustration from the poem.

WHY SHOULD I?

Why should I
Treat everyone with respect?
Why should I
Do what my parents say?
Why should I
Obey my teachers anyway?
Why should I
Be concerned about all people?
Why should I
Love instead of hate?
Why should I
Consider the feelings of others?
Why should I
Stay away from trouble?
Why should I
Be happy to help someone else?
Because I have to live
With myself!

QUESTIONS AND ACTIVITIES

1. What is respect?

2. What does it mean to be concerned?

3. Why does the student in the poem think he should do all of those things?

4. Do you do any of the things mentioned in the poem? If so, which ones do you do?

5. Which ones don't you do that you think you should work on?

6. Which one of those things do you think is the most important? Why?

7. What is the main idea of the poem?

8. In one sentence, write something you have learned from the poem.